fushigi yûgi™

The Mysterious Play
VOL. 7: CASTAWAY

Story & Art By
YUU WATASE

FUSHIGI YÛGI
THE MYSTERIOUS PLAY
VOL. 7: CASTAWAY
SHÔJO EDITION

This volume contains the FUSHIGI YÛGI installments from Animerica Extra
Vol. 4, No. 12, through Vol. 5, No. 6, in their entirety.

STORY AND ART BY YUU WATASE

Editor's Note: At the author's request, the spelling of Ms. Watase's first name has been
changed from "Yû," as it has appeared on previous VIZ publications, to "Yuu."

English Adaptation/Yuji Oniki
Translation Assist/Kaori Kawakubo Inoue
Touch-up Art & Lettering/Andy Ristaino
Design/Hidemi Sahara
Editor (1st Edition)/William Flanagan
Editor (Shôjo Edition)/Yuki Takagaki

Managing Editor/Annette Roman
Director of Production/Noboru Watanabe
Vice President of Publishing/Alvin Lu
Sr. Director of Acquisitions/Rika Inouye
Vice President of Sales & Marketing/Liza Coppola
Publisher/Hyoe Narita

Printed in Canada.

Published by VIZ, LLC
P.O. Box 77010
San Francisco, CA 94107

First edition published October 2002

Shôjo Edition
10 9 8 7 6 5 4 3 2 1
First printing, June 2005

store.viz.com

www.viz.com

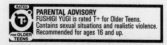

CONTENTS

STORY THUS FAR

Fifteen-year-old Miaka and her best friend Yui are physically drawn into the world of a strange book—*THE UNIVERSE OF THE FOUR GODS*. Miaka is offered the role of the lead character, the Priestess of the god Suzaku, and is charged with a mission to save the nation of Hong-Nan that will ultimately grant her any wish she wants. Yui, however, suffers rape and manipulation, which drive her to attempt suicide. Now, Yui has become the Priestess of the god Seiryu, the bitter enemy of Suzaku and Miaka.

The only way for Miaka to gain back the trust of her former best friend is to summon the god Suzaku and wish to be reconciled with Yui. But after a desperate struggle to gather her seven warriors, one warrior turns out to be a Seiryu spy, and the summoning ceremony is spoiled. But the oracle, Tai Yi-Jun, suggests a new quest to summon the god…

THE UNIVERSE OF THE FOUR GODS is based on ancient Chinese legend, but Japanese pronunciation of Chinese names differs slightly from their Chinese equivalents. Here is a short glossary of the Japanese pronunciation of the Chinese names in this graphic novel:

CHINESE	JAPANESE	PERSON OR PLACE	MEANING
Hong-Nan	Kônan	Southern Kingdom	Crimson South
Qu-Dong	Kutô	Eastern Kingdom	Gathered East
Bei-Ja	Hokkan	Northern Kingdom	Armored North
Tai Yi-Jun	Tai Itsukun	An Oracle	Preeminent Person
Shentso-Pao	Shinzahô	A Treasure	God's Seat Jewel
Ming-Ho	Meiga	A Canal	Signature Stream
Zhong-Rong	Chûei	Second Son	Loyalty & Honor
Chun-Jing	Shunkei	Third Son	Spring & Respect
Yu-Lun	Gyokuran	Eldest Daughter	Jewel & Orchid
Jie-Lian	Yuiren	Youngest Daughter	Connection & Lotus
Kang-Lin	Kôrin	A Lady of Hong-Nan	Peaceful Jewel
Liu-Chuan	Ryûen	Nuriko's Given Name	Willowy Beauty

No da: An emphatic. A verbal exclamation point placed at the end of a sentence or phrase.

CHAPTER THIRTY-SEVEN
FORBIDDEN LOVE

MIAO NIOH- AN

妙 寿 安

In the real
ancient China,
an adult male
would
have an alias
like Kanji-Kanji-
Miao Nioh-An,
but let's just
ignore that.

CORVUS

M I T S U K A K E

- Doctor in Shengshan near Changhung in northern Hong-Nan.
- Age: Currently 22 years old... looks older, though.
- Personality: Solitary
  Was in love with Shao-Huan, the daughter of a landowner in Shengshan,
  but they were never married.
- Special Power: Healing
- Hobby: Taking care of animals
- Height: 6' 6"
- Blood Type: O
- He's silent, and because he's expressionless most of the time, he's
  thought to be aloof. But he's actually just shy and doesn't know how to be
  more outgoing.
  He's very kind to the weak, as well as to animals and the elderly.
  And kids, and of course the sick. He's utterly dedicated to healing.
  A calm, kind man. Deep inside he still cherishes the memory of the
  late Shao-Huan.

SO WHAT'S A SHENTSO-PAO?

I'M NOT TELL-ING.

THAT'S RIGHT.

THEN I'LL BE ABLE TO SUMMON SUZAKU?

BEI-JIA... ...OBTAIN THE SACRED TREASURE, THE SHENTSO-PAO, IN GENBU'S COUNTRY.

OKAY, THEN! I'M GOING TO BEI-JIA!!

Y'OLD *GEEZER!*

NOW THAT THE CEREMONY HAS FAILED, I'LL DO ANYTHING FOR ANOTHER CHANCE TO SUMMON SUZAKU.

THEN IF YOU'RE DECIDED...

THAT'S "SHENTSO-PAO!"...

I'M HAVING MY DOUBTS AGAIN.

I'M **GOING** TO FIND THAT CHEAPO POLE!

!?

YOU GET NOTHING!

HMPH

THAT'S GREAT, TAI YI-JUN!

WHAT ABOUT ME!?

Y'KNOW, FER SOME REASON I *DO* FEEL MORE POWERFUL!

HOW YOU USE THEM IS UP TO YOU.

YOUR POWERS HAVE BEEN IN-CREASED.

...SINCE A GIFT FROM THIS "*GEEZER*" WON'T HELP YOUR MONEY-GRUBBING SCHEMES.

HO HO HO

THERE'S NOTHING SPECIAL PREPARED FOR YOU...

CLOSE YOUR EYES, MIAKA.

OH, ONE LAST THING. I ALMOST FORGOT...

AFTER ALL I'VE BEEN THROUGH?

ひょろりらら

YOU'RE KIDDING!

GIMME THAT! I WANT IT!

ASH?

IF YOU HAVE ANY SPECIAL POWER, THIS WILL ENABLE YOU EVENTUALLY TO UTILIZE IT.

IT'S THE SPECIAL ASH FROM THE BURNT REMAINS OF *THE UNIVERSE OF THE FOUR GODS.*

DON'T WORRY, IT ISN'T HOT.

Now, we've finally reached Volume 7. Looking over the covers of these graphic novels, I can't help but be moved. After finishing chapter 42 (the last chapter in this volume), I went to China to do some research. Only three days after returning, I had to attend a shōjo manga event, so I had a pretty rough summer. I'd like to thank you all for coming to the event. Those of you who live in the provinces, if you're upset the event was held in Tokyo, I'm sure you'll have an opportunity. (Actually I've appeared in events in Sendai, Nagoya and twice on my home turf in Osaka, so I might show up somewhere in your region.) Some of my fans traveled from far, far away to attend the event, but I have to say I was surprised by the fan who came from Taiwan! She tried so hard to talk to me in Japanese... That's right! Because "Fushigi" is published in Taiwan, I have been receiving the occasional fan mail from over there. Of course I can't read any of it. So I had my editor get a Taiwanese copy of "Prepubescence" (the Japanese title is "Shishun-ki Miman Okotowari," but over there it's "Si Chun Qi Wei Man"). It was incredible, because Asuka and the others are all speaking Taiwanese! Even these one-third-page free-talk sections were translated. "Fushigi Yûgi" is called "Meng Huan Yiou Xi" or "Dream Play" (this actually sounds cooler), and the free-talk sections should be translated, too! I would like to thank all my readers in Taiwan!

COUNT *ME* IN, TOO...

THANKS...

TAMA-HOME!

HOLD IT! HOLD IT! *HOLD IT!*

どたたたた

WELL, I GOTTA GO *PACK!!*

FORGIVE THE INTER-RUPTION.

HOWEVER, WE MAY HAVE TROUBLE...

THE REST OF YOU, LEAVE!

I NEED TO SPEAK WITH THE PRIESTESS PRIVATELY!

I'VE GOT MORE TO TELL YOU.

WHAT'S WRONG?

IT'S NOT LIKE YOU TO BE ANXIOUS...

YOUR EMINENCE!

BE THAT AS IT MAY, PLEASE COME WITH ME.

14

Castaway

IT APPEARS THAT AMI-BOSHI... SUBOSHI'S TWIN BROTHER...

WHAT'S HE DOING...

!?

KREEK

...HAS DIED.

DIED!? WHAT ...!?

IT SEEMS HE WAS KILLED BY THE SUZAKU CELESTIAL WARRIORS. I TRIED SEARCHING FOR HIS CHI AS WELL, BUT I WAS UNABLE TO...

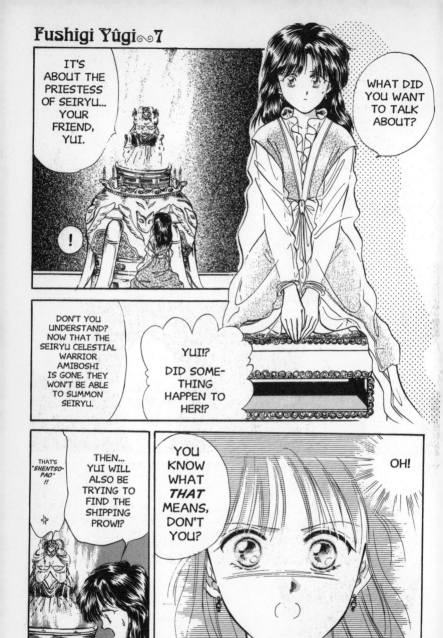

IT'S ABOUT THE PRIESTESS OF SEIRYU... YOUR FRIEND, YUI.

WHAT DID YOU WANT TO TALK ABOUT?

!

DON'T YOU UNDERSTAND? NOW THAT THE SEIRYU CELESTIAL WARRIOR AMIBOSHI IS GONE, THEY WON'T BE ABLE TO SUMMON SEIRYU.

YUI!? DID SOME-THING HAPPEN TO HER!?

THAT'S "SHENTSO-PAO" !!

THEN... YUI WILL ALSO BE TRYING TO FIND THE SHIPPING PROW!?

YOU KNOW WHAT *THAT* MEANS, DON'T YOU?

OH!

19

FIGHT YUI...

WHICH ONE OF US WILL RETRIEVE THE SHENTSO-PAO FIRST...?

YOU MENTIONED HARD-SHIPS...

THAT'S WHAT YOU MEANT?

ONE MORE THING...

YOU MUST LISTEN CLOSELY.

YUI'S MY MORTAL ENEMY!

IF SHE IS ALSO SEARCHING, YOU TWO WILL BE MORTAL ENEMIES!!

YOU MAY HAVE TO FIGHT THE SEIRYU WARRIORS!

THIS MAY BE...

...EVEN MORE DIFFICULT TO BEAR.

I WAS COOPED UP AT HOME STUDYING FOR MY EXAMS.

YOU WERE LIVING IN ZHUANG-YUAN!? THAT'S ONLY A STONE'S THROW FROM THE CAPITAL.

WHAT'S TAKING MIAKA SO LONG?

AHH, MIND YER OWN BUSINESS!

HEY TASUKI, WHY DON'T YOU STOP THIEVING A WHILE AND GIVE STUDYING A TRY?

PROOF THAT GREEDINESS IS WORSE THAN BANDITRY.

BE FAIR! I DIDN'T GET ANYTHING!

WHAT'RE YOU DOING!?

WAAAH!!

SNEAK SNEAK

KREEK

WHEN THIS IS ALL OVER, I'M GOING BACK TO LIGÉ-SAN MOUNTAIN TO BE THE BEST BOSS THERE EVER WAS!

THAT'S WHY THIS HARISEN...

EH?

YEAH.

LET'S GO BACK TO THE PALACE. I'M A LITTLE WIPED!

MIAKA, IS THE AUDIENCE OVER?

MIAKA ...?

OF COURSE.

23

DAMN, I THOUGHT YOU WERE SNEAKING IN FOR A QUICKIE.

NO. I JUST WANTED TO SEE YOU.

A *NORMAL* GIRL WOULD HAVE SCREAMED!

I WAS WITH CHICHIRI DISCUSSING HOW WE'D GET TO BEI-JIA.

IT'S PRETTY LATE. IS SOMETHING THE MATTER?

NOTHING AT ALL...

DID YOU SAY SOMETHING?

...

24

I WAS JUST THINKING HOW NICE IT WOULD BE IF WE WERE ALWAYS LIKE THIS.

WH-WHAT'S WRONG!? IS THERE SOMETHING IN MY TEETH?

NO.

HM?

YEAH...

?

I'VE BEEN SENDING MONEY HOME, BUT I'VE ALSO BEEN PUTTING A LITTLE ASIDE FOR MYSELF.

MIAKA...

SO... I'D LIKE TO...

...BUILD MYSELF A HOUSE...

...AND LIVE A HUMBLE-BUT-HAPPY LIFE.

AND SO...

I MEAN, I'M REACHING THAT AGE WHEN, YOU KNOW...

...WHEN I WANT TO STRIKE OUT ON MY OWN.

YEAH... UH-HUH...

ごくごくごく ← NOT LISTENING.

ブッブッ

...AND KIDS, A BOY WOULD BE NICE, BUT THAT'S JUST ME BEING SELFISH...

I-IN OTHER WORDS...

WHAT I'M SAYING IS...

27

32

WHY...?

THAT'S WHAT I CAME TO TELL YOU TONIGHT.

OKAY...

WHY!?

GOOD-NIGHT, TAMAHOME.

MIAKA ...

I said before that I dreamed of this: Nakago in a uniform! ♥♥

Seems a little too blocky...

I don't know why, but in my dream he was wearing dark sunglasses. ◊

...e looks so good in black! ...love it!! ♥♥♥ ...But people are beginning to dislike him! I've had several letters saying, "I love the way he looks, but..." and one ad- dressed to "Mr. Sadist Nakago"! ◊ On the other hand, someone else said, "He's cruel, he can only get better!" Anyway, of all the Fushigi Yûgi characters, Nakago ranks No. 1!!

Writers just seem to love bad guys and side characters

A man who looks good with a whip! NAKAGO's

CHAPTER THIRTY-EIGHT

THE NIGHT OF THE STAR-GAZING FESTIVAL

"PLEASE DO ME THE HONOR OF LIVING IN THAT HOUSE."

I DIDN'T SLEEP A WINK...

TAMA-HOME, IF I COULD ONLY *BE* YOUR WIFE...

IF I COULD SPEND THE REST OF MY LIFE WITH YOU...

Now, I'm going to tell you how I ended up owning a dog. It first started as an impulse-- I just wanted a dog. Then I started getting specific, thinking a small one would be nice. We once took care of my uncle's Yorkshire Terrier for a couple of days, so I automatically thought, "That breed is the one to get!" They're supposed to be pretty smart as far as dogs go... A tiny, fist-sized, trembling, three-month-old puppy arrived. By the way, she's female. As for her name...my parents were required to register her name at the shop, so the best they could come up with was "Yuu." They're such space cadets using my name! So we're giving her name a different kanji character. (I just noticed recently how it's the same "Yû" for Fushigi Yûgi.) I have to say, it's really hard to train dogs. ♪ (I hope potty training goes okay.) When the dog doesn't behave, we have to spank and scold her. But she's so tiny and cute--it's hard! So, now it's been six months, and she hasn't grown much at all.
(Well...compared to the beginning when she was smaller than a slipper, I guess she has...) She's not really crazy about food. Maybe she doesn't have much of an appetite, or maybe she's just fickle. She never cries, even when she's hungry.
But she stares at you when you say something to her, so maybe she knows more than she's letting on.

GOOD MORNING, TAMA-HOME.

...

I HAVE TO THINK ABOUT...

IT'S BEST FOR US THIS WAY.

...HOW THE PRIESTESS OF SEIRYU AND I "WILL BE MORTAL ENEMIES"!!

THERE'S A FESTIVAL TONIGHT.

LET'S ALL GO TOGETHER, OKAY?

TELL US HOW YA **BLEW IT!** C'MON!!

KNOWING YOU, I'M SURE YOU WERE WAY TOO AGGRES- SIVE!

TOMP

IMITATING MIAKA

DIDYA SEE THAT, NURIKO? THAT LOOKED **REALLY** AWKWARD.

ABSO- LUTELY, TASUKI. SHE **TOTALLY** IGNORED HIM!

BEI-JIA IS A MOUN- TAINOUS REGION...

I-I GUESS... HE **DID** BLOW IT...

41

CHI-CHIRI...

!

SUBOSHI?

I'M VERY SORRY... ABOUT YESTER-DAY...

WHAT ARE YOU DOING HERE?

ATTEN--SHUT!

...I WAS VERY RUDE, AND...

THAT'S OKAY. I'M FINE.

I'M GLAD TO SEE YOU'RE LOOKING BETTER.

Y-YES...

NAKAGO... WANTED ME TO TAKE YOU TO THE SEIRYU SHRINE.

WHAT ARE YOU DOING, NAKAGO!?

47

ピチチチ‼

・・・

ARE THERE... FISH IN THIS POND?

・・・

DUNNO.

NO DA.

WITH THE MASK ON, YOU CAN SMILE ALL THE TIME.

IT'S CUTE, TOO.

I'M SORRY! IF YOU DON'T WANT TO TALK ABOUT IT, THAT'S FINE!!

・・・

I'VE BEEN WONDER- ING...

...WHY YOU WEAR A MASK.

I WAS THINKING THAT I'D LIKE ONE.

48

...I WAS ENGAGED TO A VERY SPECIAL GIRL. SHE, MY BEST FRIEND AND I... THE THREE OF US WERE VERY CLOSE.

NO DA.

I WAS EIGHTEEN AND A BOY LIKE TAMA-HOME...

THE ONE WHO I THOUGHT WAS MY BEST FRIEND... ENDED UP STEALING HER AWAY.

BUT THAT ALL CAME TO AN END ONE DAY.

I HAD A VERY QUICK TEMPER BACK THEN. I FELT SO MUCH ANGER, SADNESS AND BETRAYAL THAT I LOST CONTROL.

THEN WHAT HAPPENED?

...MY BEST FRIEND... WITH THESE VERY HANDS.

I KILLED...

SHE LOVES YOU SO MUCH, SHE ENDED UP HATING YOU ALL THE MORE.

SO YOU MUST HELP HER.

NO DA.

MORE THAN YOU KNOW... SHE HERSELF MIGHT NOT EVEN BE AWARE OF IT.

THE ONLY THING I CAN SAY IS THAT...

...YUI LOVES YOU.

...I DON'T QUITE GET WHAT YOU'RE SAYING, BUT I'LL THINK IT OVER!

THANKS FOR LISTEN- ING!

...

MIAKA! ME-AARDVARK! ME-ANTHILL!

MIAKA!

?

WHAT IS YOUR PROBLEM!?

TUG

NO DA!

WOW! I'VE NEVER SEEN THE CITY AT NIGHT!

HAK

HE'S JUST MOPING.

LET 'IM BE.

IT WOULDN'T HAVE HURT TAMAHOME TO COME!

ONCE WE'RE UNDERWAY, WE WON'T HAVE ANY TIME FOR REST.

THAT'S RIGHT.

NURIKO'S DOING THIS FOR US!

IT'S ONLY A SHORT BREAK.

LET'S ENJOY IT!

CAUGH CAUGH

HEY, WHAT'S GOING ON!?

A STRENGTH COMPETI- TION. THE WINNER GETS A PRIZE.

WOW! LOOKIT THAT!

HMPH!

HURRAY!

YEEAAAHH!!

TONIGHT WE ARE GOING TO *PAR-TAY!*

55

HA HA HA!

THAT MAKES *ME* THE WINNER!

THERE AIN'T *NOBODY* ELSE THAT CAN DO BETTER!

GRIN

HUP!

WAAHHH!

LOOKEE, LOOKEE!

I GOT THE GRAND PRIZE!

ALL RIGHT, MIAKA! NOW LET'S SEE THE PER-FORMERS!!

AN' THE GAL JUMPS IN AND *WINS!*

HELP! LEMME DOWN! LEMME DOWN!

57

OR ELSE, I'LL **FORCE** YOU TO CONFRONT MY DAD!

TELL ME SO I CAN UNDER-STAND.

NOTHING...

NOTH--

YOU'RE LYING!! I ASKED YOU TO **MARRY ME!** DO YOU EXPECT ME TO GIVE UP THAT EASILY!?

"ONE MORE THING... YOU MUST LISTEN CARE-FULLY."

THIS MAY BE... EVEN MORE DIFFICULT TO BEAR.

WH-WHAT IS!?

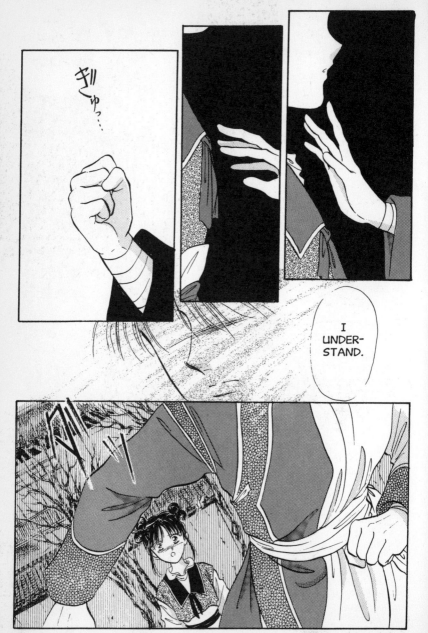

ALL RIGHT, MIAKA!

UNTIL YOU SUMMON SUZAKU...

...I'LL PROTECT YOU AS A CELESTIAL WARRIOR.

...I'LL MAKE YOU THE HAPPIEST BRIDE THE WORLD HAS EVER SEEN.

BUT THE VERY *MOMENT* SUZAKU APPEARS...

EYAAAH!!

Y- YOU'RE *AWFUL!*

CAN YOU *TRY* NOT TO PLAY FLAT!?

CAUGHT IN THE POWERS OF THE FALSE CHIRIKO'S "SONG OF MASS MURDER," THE CELESTIAL WARRIORS SUFFER THEIR WORST NIGHTMARE!!

FUSHIGI AKUGI
THE MALICIOUS PLAY

NO. 7

SUGGESTED BY...A READER.

I WANTED TO PUT IN THE READER'S NAME, BUT BY THE TIME I WAS MAKING UP THIS PAGE MY MOM HAD FILED THE LETTER AWAY, AND I CAN'T FIND IT ANYMORE!

I'M SO SORRY!! ◊

This seems like an obvious joke, but I only got two messages suggesting it. Still, it's really funny. One person's suggestion was much the same. Despite Miaka's complaining ☺ the characters really could die from the song.

WHERE? WHERE? WHERE?

BOX

There were several other really funny suggestions, but we'll leave them for later.

*Oh! I didn't get the chance to mention this in the chat sections, but thanks to everyone who bought the FY CD book! I hear the reviews were mostly favorable.◊ I had no complaints with the voice actors. By the way, did you notice Tamahome's song, "Kimi o Mamoritai" ("I Want to Protect You")? At the end of the second verse, during the bridge, there were some words with digital effects over them. They were "unmei," ("fate"), "densetsu" ("legend"), "kiseki no hito" ("miraculous one"), "shukumei" ("destiny"), and "seiza no sadame" ("fortune of the stars").

Probably! Oh, and of the seven images in the FY Calendar, six are originals that I still have to draw! 👁👁

Until next time!

CHAPTER THIRTY-NINE
FRAIL SMILE

OH?

A-AIN'T *NOTHIN'* THE MATTER WITH ME.

HEY, WHAT'S THE MATTER, TASUKI?

...

AND TOMOR- ROW'S THE BIG DAY!

YOUR SWEAT GIVES YOU AWAY!

HA HA HA!

WHAT ABSURDITY!

WH-WHY, WHATEVER ARE YA TALKING ABOUT, SEÑOR? ME? UNABLE TO SWIM? HOW PATHETIC D'YA THINK I AM!?

I GET IT!!

YOU CAN'T SWIM!!

SHE SHOULD BE PACKING RIGHT NOW...

AND WHERE IS MIAKA?

AIEEE!! HELP!!

GO!

LET'S SEE.

MY FLASH-LIGHT... MY UNDER-WEAR...

BETTER BRING LOTS OF SNACKS!

SIGH

I GUESS I GOTTA BRING THESE DRILL BOOKS, TOO.

I GOTTA TAKE THOSE EXAMS.

"MOM, I'M HOME!"

THANK YOU, YOUR MAJESTY.

I HAVE *FAITH* THAT YOU *WILL* SUMMON SEIRYU.

DO YOU UNDERSTAND MY MEANING?

NAKAGO, YOU HAVE BROUGHT MANY VICTORIES TO MY EMPIRE.

VERY WELL THEN...GO.

LET ME KNOW IF THERE IS ANYTHING YOU NEED.

I SWEAR TO YOU THAT THIS TIME, YOUR MAJESTY'S FAITH WON'T BE MIS-PLACED.

YES!

TEE HEE!

OH, YOUR MAJESTY!

SUBOSHI! WHERE ARE YOU GOING!?

I ORDERED YOU TO STAY WITH YUI.

HOW CAN I SIT STILL WHILE AMIBOSHI'S MURDERER GOES UNPUNISHED!?

!

WHAT CAN YOU DO ALONE? UNLIKE YOUR BROTHER, YOU HAVEN'T MASTERED YOUR SKILLS.

DON'T UNDERESTIMATE THE SUZAKU CELESTIAL WARRIORS.

YOU'RE SEEKING VEN- GEANCE?

I DO UNDERSTAND ...HOW YOU FEEL.

HOWEVER...

NAKAGO!

NOTHING, YOUR EMINENCE.

HAVE YOU DECIDED TO JOURNEY TO BEI-JIA?

THERE YOU ARE SUBOSHI!

WHAT'S WRONG?

BESIDES, I DON'T THINK MIAKA'S GOING THERE.

I DOUBT SHE WANTS TO FIGHT ME.

I DIDN'T BECOME THE PRIESTESS OF SEIRYU IN ORDER TO SUMMON THE GOD.

YOU MAY FIND YOU ARE ALONE IN THAT ASSUMPTION.

HEH!

HEY, WHAT AM I DOING THERE!?

AN INSTANT CAMERA.

INSTINCT- IVELY THE THREE OF THEM POSE.

WHAT'S THAT?

CAPTURED THE MOMENT!

HA HA HAA!

THE OTHER WORLD HAS SOME PRETTY AMAZING STUFF.

WHAT'S THE BIG DEAL?

THAT GUY'S A FAKE!

I'M THE REAL ME!!

GASP

I ALMOST FORGOT... WE AREN'T ALLOWED TO TOUCH...

...THE LINE BETWEEN THE PRIESTESS AND THE CELESTIAL WARRIORS CAN'T BE CROSSED.

"THE BODY OF THE PRIESTESS OF SUZAKU MUST BE PURE!

SHE MUST BE A VIRGIN."

HEY, CHI-CHIRI, COME JOIN US!

TAKE EIGHT PHOTOS SO EVERYONE GETS ONE.

S-SO, I PRESS HERE?

CLIK

LOOK HOW CLOSE WE ARE, BUT...

PUTTING ON A SMILE

A THOUGHT CAME TO US LAST NIGHT...

...CONCERNING YOUR FAMILY.

WHAT?

TAMAHOME...

I KNOW I GOTTA SUMMON SUZAKU, BUT I DON'T WANT TO FIGHT YUI!!

WHAT'M I SUPPOSED TO DO!?

SHE'S PROBABLY HUNGRY AGAIN.

WHAT'S WRONG WITH HER?

THIS IS NOT CHARITY.

THEY PROVIDED US HOSPITALITY.

WE WISH TO RETURN THE FAVOR.

WHILE YOU ARE ABROAD, YOU WILL BE ANXIOUS ABOUT THEM, NO?

THE CROWN CAN PROVIDE THEM WITH A HOUSE IN THE CITY.

!

SHALL WE BRING THEM HERE?

THANK...

THANK YOU, YOUR MAJESTY!!

AWESOME, HOTOHORI!!

YOU *SOFTIE*, YOU!

NOOGIE NOOGIE NOOGIE NOOGIE

UHH, WELL...

THANK YOU! THANK YOU! THANK YOU!

I'M FOREVER IN YOUR DEBT!

Most dogs like to be hugged, right? Ours doesn't. I wonder why. She loves sleeping on the futon. She'll lie on a towel like it's a pillow or use it like a blanket to cover up. Sometimes I can't help but think, "Are you human or what!?"

I didn't realize how cute dogs can be. But now I know why pet owners the world over are so crazy about their cats and dogs-- on international TV and the like. The pets become part of the family.

A friend of mine was telling me how dogs emit alpha waves (?), so they have a stress-reducing effect when you pet them. I don't know if that's true, but it is true that hugging dogs or petting them makes you feel better, even when you're angry. Also, when you stare at their kind eyes, you feel all warm inside. Animals are so wonderful. But when they pass away, it can be painful. I heard a story about a kid who brought his pet dog, who had just died, to the toy store and asked the owner there to "Please, fix him." Come on! Animals aren't machines! I'm sure teaching children about the importance of life and death is a difficult under-taking, but give me a break! Someone else stuck his dead dog in a microwave to warm it.

Let's get with it, people!

I WONDER WHAT'LL MAKE JIE-LIAN HAPPY?

NO GOOD!

HE'S GONE BYE-BYE.

BETTER LEAVE HIM ALONE.

I ALREADY BOUGHT HER A DOLL.

YOU REALLY LIKE JIE-LIAN, DON'T YOU!

HMM?

I LIKE THEM ALL BUT... *HA HA...*

•••

MOM DIED AFTER JIE-LIAN WAS BORN, SO I WAS THE ONE WHO ENDED UP RAISING HER.

I GUESS... I'M A LITTLE JEALOUS.

LET'S SEE...

I'M SO SORRY! I WAS GETTING CARRIED AWAY.

OH, IT'S OKAY! LET *ME* CHOOSE SOMETHING.

...WOULD BE A GOOD CHOICE.

PERHAPS THIS BALL...

GEEZ... YOU REALLY TOOK US BY SURPRISE.

CHAPTER FORTY
VOW ON A GRAVE

Speaking of life, I remember that there was quite a reaction to "The Jie-Lian Family Massacre" (that sounds weird ♪) in this episode...One reader's letter began, "It can't be true" and ended, "It's too terrible!" Apparently, her friend was reading it lying down and lost her contact lens from crying. Of course, I couldn't draw the scene without crying, too, you know! You might ask, "Then why did you have to draw it!?" Well, that's how stories work (that's the reason?). Tamahome, who watched helplessly as Jie-Lian died in his arms, must be the saddest one though...

Getting back to my dog, while I was at my office (near my house), Yuu, who had just learned how to climb the stairs, fell from the second floor. My mother immediately came to the rescue, and as soon as she saw Yuu not moving and with her tongue hanging out, she thought the dog was dead! Yuu was only unconscious, though. She moved a little, and my mother held her until the vet arrived. In the meantime, Yuu was trying to tell her something in a strange voice. An excuse!? My mom, the one who yells the most in our family, started to cry, afraid that Yuu might die. The dog was put on an IV at the vet's and she recovered...

It totally freaked me out.

NOW, IT'S YOUR TIME TO DIE!!

KIDS JUST DON'T LISTEN TO THEIR ELDERS THESE DAYS!

I'M NOT INTERESTED IN YOUR TRANSPARENT LIES!

KRAKK

TAMA-
HOME!!

TSK!

IS
THAT...

...HOW
YOU
KILLED
THEM?

NO!

IF ONLY I HAD SPECIAL POWERS...

...I COULD FIGHT, TOO!!

TAMA-HOME!!

...ALL YOU'VE GOT!?

IS THAT...

...

111

112

ARE YOU ALL RIGHT?

NURI-KO...

WHERE'S TAMA-HOME?

PL!S

MIAKA!

AND WHERE ARE THE *NEIGHBORS!?* WITH ALL THIS COMMOTION, DON'T TELL ME NOBODY NOTICED!

NO HUMAN *WARMTH* AROUND HERE!

...

WHAT A THING TO HAPPEN, JUST BEFORE SETTING OUT.

HE'S NOT HURT. HE WENT TO BURY HIS FAMILY.

THEY'RE JUST NORMAL PEOPLE... THEY'RE SCARED...

WHAT
CAN I
DO?

KRCH KRCH

...THAT
WOULD
MAKE IT
ANY
BETTER?

WHAT
CAN I
SAY...

UH...

HEY...

119

A DIP IN THE SEA MIGHT ACTUALLY BE GOOD FOR HIM.

NO DA.

AIEEE! HELP MEEE!

I TOLD YOU NOT TO TEASE HIM.

YOU SHOULD BE CAREFUL, TOO, HOTOHORI. THE ENEMY COULD SHOW UP *ANYWHERE.*

HA HA! YOU IDIOT.

I SEE... HOW HORRIBLE.

ME? I'LL BE ALL RIGHT! I'M READY FOR THIS.

I AM PREPARED. MY CONCERN IS FOR YOU AND THE OTHERS.

I WON'T LET YOU DIE WHILE I LIVE.

"PRIESTESS, PLEASE TELL MY SON THIS."

"YOU MUST LIVE HONORABLY AS A CELESTIAL WARRIOR. YOU ARE OUR PRIDE."

WE'LL RETRIEVE THE SHENTSO-PAO...

...AND WE'LL ALL COME BACK HERE SAFELY!

AND I'LL PROTECT *YOU!*

MAY THEY HAVE A SAFE JOURNEY.

THEY'RE GONE.

LOOKS LIKE OUR DOG.

THE PRIESTESS OF SUZAKU IS DETERMINED TO BECOME YOUR ENEMY.

DO YOU SEE NOW, YOUR EMINENCE?

MIAKA...

...IS HEADING TO BEI-JIA?

SHE WANTS THE SHENTSO-PAO, EVEN IF IT MEANS YOUR DEFEAT.

YOU MUST NOW MAKE A DECISION...

138

CHAPTER FORTY-ONE
THE MYSTERY OF "THE UNIVERSE OF THE FOUR GODS"

BA-BAN

MAYBE... WE SHOULD COOK AFTER ALL...

SO I CAN'T COOK! SUE ME!

YOU LITTLE BIGOT!!

HYAAH!

POW

BIFF

DON'T TELL ME... YOU'RE SEASICK?

...

BINGO!

DOES ANYBODY HAVE SOMETHING TO KEEP A GUY'S LUNCH DOWN?

DOES...

NURIKO... THE MINUTE I FEEL LIKE LIVIN', YOU'RE DEAD!

SO THE BIG BRAWNY BANDIT LEADER IS SEASICK!!

BWA HA HA HA HA HA

NOPE.

BLUNTLY...

GONNG

YOU GOTTA HAVE MEDICINE FOR SEASICK- NESS!

MITSUKAKE, THANK TH' GODS!

EH?

O-OH NO!!

NOT IN HERE!! IT'LL GET MIXED UP WITH THE FOOD.

WISH I HAD THEIR ENERGY...

DON'T GROSS ME OUT, FOOL!

❧ Castaway ❧

Because of the scary experience she had, I thought my dog would be too scared to go near the stairs. But soon enough she started climbing them again. Well, she did stop following everyone around, so I guess she learned something. I just wish she'd go to the bathroom properly. Please don't pee just to get attention!! ♭ And so my dog story comes to an end. Now, should I share another "Fushigi" story? Oh, we received a lot of complaints after the bonus pages weren't included in volume 5. It was simply because there were so many pages of art that the bonus pages and chapter title pages wouldn't fit into the book. (The number of pages in a graphic novel is limited.) If we added bonus pages, we would have to cut manga pages, so we really had no choice but to leave them out. I'm so sorry! It's nice to know how important those pages are to you. In fact, the very reason I title each chapter was so the graphic novels would have room for bonus pages.

I've been receiving all sorts of questions, but a lot of them I just can't answer. ♪ I think that if I had to answer them all, I wouldn't find time to draw anymore! But many of your questions will be answered as the story unfolds, so please be patient and enjoy it! Your question will probably be answered in the future. You'll see.

The story's constructed like a puzzle.

NO!!

EYYOOWW!!

THWUMP

THE UNIVERSE OF THE FOUR GODS

JAPANESE TRANSLATION BY EINOSUKE OKUDA

すたすたすたすた すたすたすたすた

...

PERFECT TIMING! I NEED THAT ¥10,000 I LENT YOU FOR THAT PARTY!

THERE YOU ARE, TETSUYA!

YOU *DO* HEAR ME!!

WHERE? WHERE?

CHECK OUT THE HOT BABE!!

YOUR SISTER WAS SUCKED INTO A *BOOK*!?

WHAT !?

REALLY BUSY! CAN'T TALK! GOTTA GO!

THERE'S NO ESCAPE FOR YOU!

图書館
LIBRARY

SHH! LOWER YOUR VOICE, WILL YA?

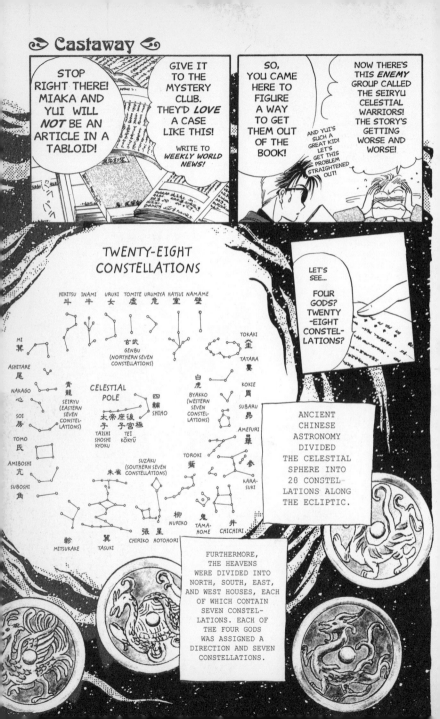

LONG AGO, THE CHINESE PEOPLE THOUGHT THAT IF THERE WERE IRREGULARITIES IN THESE STAR HOUSES—THE CONSTELLATIONS—THEN IT PORTENDED DANGER.

I GET IT... IF YOUR SISTER'S THIS "PRIESTESS," THEN "SUZAKU" HAS TO BE THE "SACRED BEAST" OF THE SOUTHERN CONSTELLATIONS.

THIS BOOK IS A JAPANESE TRANSLATION, SO THERE'S GOTTA BE A CHINESE ORIGINAL SOMEWHERE...

SO IT'S NO WONDER THEY STARTED WORSHIPPING THE FOUR AS GODS.

COULD BE IN HERE...

THE TRANSLATOR'S EINOSUKE OKUDA. IF WE CHECK HIM OUT, WE MIGHT FIND SOME CLUES.

奥田　永之介

EINOSUKE OKUDA

WAIT A SEC... *THE UNIVERSE OF THE FOUR GODS* ISN'T LISTED IN THE WORKS HE'S CREDITED WITH.

TAISHO!? THAT'S SEVENTY OR EIGHTY YEARS AGO!

THERE HE IS! HMMM... A TRANSLATOR FROM THE TAISHO* ERA?

*TAISHO ERA: 1912–1926.

146

AND LOOK! ***THE UNIVERSE OF THE FOUR GODS*** DOESN'T HAVE AN ENTRY IN THE CATALOG OF JAPANESE PUBLICATIONS!

THAT'S IMPOSSIBLE! I'M HOLDING THE BOOK IN MY HANDS!

SHHHHHHHH!

YOU'RE ***KID-DING!***

...HE MURDERED HIS ONLY DAUGHTER TAKIKO, THEN COMMITTED SUICIDE.

OH...HOLD IT. HE WAS RESPONSIBLE FOR ***THE CHINESE RIVER SAGA***, AMONG OTHER ACADEMIC WORKS, BUT IN 1923, THE TWELFTH YEAR OF TAISHO...

ALL RECORDS OF ***THE UNIVERSE OF THE FOUR GODS*** WERE ERASED...

...AND THE TRANSLATOR KILLED HIS DAUGHTER, THEN HIMSELF.

じっかり

T-TAMA-HOME!

THE MAN IS *HOPELESS!*

YOU'D BETTER BE ASLEEP FOR REAL.

HE'S NOT DOING IT ON PURPOSE, SO I CAN ALLOW IT THIS TIME...

BUT SHE'S STILL HAPPY ABOUT IT.

L-LET *GO* OF ME!!

...WE COULD LOVE EACH OTHER WITHOUT RESTRIC-TIONS.

IF THIS WERE THE *NORMAL* WORLD...

...AND TAMAHOME WAS A *NORMAL* HIGH-SCHOOL KID...

150

MMM?

POPP

UH...
UM...

TOTALLY
FLUSTERED

•••

OH, *MAN!!*
MY DREAM
SELF USUALLY
TRIES TO GO
ALL THE WAY!
WHAT'S WRONG
WITH ME?

YOU
TRIED
TO TAKE
ADVANTAGE
OF ME
IN MY
SLEEP!!

HOW ICKY!

YOU
WISH!!
I BROUGHT
YOU SOME FOOD,
AND YOU
GRABBED ME
IN YOUR
SLEEP!!

YOU
MASHER!!

ACCORDING TO THEIR BELIEFS, THE SACRED BEASTS APPEAR AT THE BORDER BETWEEN BOTH OPPOSITES OF HEAVEN AND EARTH, AND SHADOW AND LIGHT. THEIR RITUALS WERE BASED ON ANCIENT ASTROLOGY, WHICH BREAKS DOWN THE HEAVENS INTO 28 CONSTELLATIONS, WHICH ARE THEN DIVIDED INTO FOUR HOUSES OF SEVEN CONSTELLATIONS.

ONE MAY FIND WORSHIP OF THE FOUR GODS PRACTICED AMONG THE HERETICS.

L-LOOK AT *THIS...*

DO YOU GOTTA STRANGLE ME EVERY TIME?

HEY!! THIS IS THE SAME ASTROLOGY AS IN MIAKA'S BOOK!!

...THEY GATHERED INCANTATIONS THAT WOULD SUMMON EACH OF THE FOUR SACRED BEASTS AND RECORDED THEM.

THE SCRIPTURE THAT CONTAINS THESE INCANTATIONS IS CALLED **THE UNIVERSE OF THE FOUR GODS.**

KEISUKE...?

MIAKA!

KEISUKE... KEISUKE, IS THAT YOU!?

EH?

THE UNIVERSE OF THE FOUR GODS IS DANGEROUS!!

MIAKA!! COME BACK TO THIS WORLD NOW!!

WHAT'S WITH HIM?

I GOT EXAMS!

SHAD-DUP!

WHAT'S COME OVER HER?

I DON'T KNOW. ALL OF A SUDDEN--

KILLED?

IF I'M RIGHT...

...YOU AND YUI ARE IN TROUBLE!

YOU MIGHT EVEN GET YOUR-SELVES *KILLED!!*

WHAT'S THE MATTER, CHIRIKO?

NO DA?

MIAKA? STRANGE?

SHE'S ALWAYS STRANGE. NO DA.

MIAKA'S ACTING STRANGELY...

CAN I ABANDON THEM?

DO YOU WANT TO DIE, MIAKA?

MIAKA, ARE YOU ALL RIGHT!?

I'LL BET YOU ATE SOMETHING OFF THE FLOOR!

YER PROBABLY RIGHT!

"I STILL HAVE SOME-BODY! YOU."

MIAKA?

JIE-LIAN...

I'M GOING TO FIND OUT *EVERYTHING!* STARTING WITH EINOSUKE OKUDA'S SUICIDE...

I *WILL* GET MIAKA AND YUI BACK HERE!!

H-HEY, THAT RIBBON BURNED UP BY *ITSELF*...

THE LITTLE *IDIOT*...

WHAT DID... I NEVER...

NOW, I'VE COMPLETELY CUT MY CONNECTION TO KEISUKE...

MIAKA... THAT WAS THE TIE TO *YOUR* WORLD...

THAT *DOES* IT. YOU'RE COMING WITH *ME!*

HEY, KEISUKE! WHERE'RE YOU GOING!?

163

THIS IS HOW THE FY CHARACTERS WOULD LOOK IN NORMAL HIGH-SCHOOL UNIFORMS.

THE OTHER CHARACTERS JUST DON'T LOOK GOOD IN THEM!

AMIBOSHI

HE WAS MUCH MORE POPULAR THAN I REALIZED, AND WHEN HE DIED, THERE WERE A LOT OF LETTERS OF PROTEST!

TAMAHOME

TASUKI

THESE TWO LOOK LIKE STREET PUNKS!

CHAPTER FORTY-TWO
REMINISCENCE OF THE FUTURE

WATCH
OUT!
WE'RE
GONNA
HIT THE
ROCKS!!

YAAH!!!

166

DAMN HER! WHERE IS SHE!?

ONE OF THE SEIRYU CELESTIAL WARRIORS! SHE CONTROLS LIGHTNING!

WHAZZAT!?

LIGHTNING... IS SOI BEHIND THIS!?

...

HEH.

THAT THUNDERCLOUD WILL FOLLOW YOU UNTIL YOUR SHIP IS DESTROYED OR ETERNITY CLAIMS YOU.

YOU'LL BE SWALLOWED WHOLE BY THE WATERS BEFORE YOU EVER REACH BEI-JIA!

WHAT'S A LITTLE HARMLESS WATER!?

WE'RE TAKING ON WATER!!

MIAKA!!

SHI-- BLUR BLURB!

REKKA...

MY *FIRE* CAN EVAPORATE IT!!

TASUKI!!

I CAN'T SWIM!!

169

HEY, WE'RE STILL *ALIVE* OVER HERE!!

NGGH! I WON'T FORGET...THE *SACRIFICE* YOU THREE MADE FER ME!!

!!

MIAKA, ARE YOU ALL RIGHT!?

THEY'RE BEING CARRIED AWAY!

WE HAVE TO GO AFTER!

WE GOTTA KEEP THEM FROM GETTING FARTHER AWAY...

IF THE LIGHTNING STRIKES NOW, THEY'LL BE ELECTROCUTED!

NO DA!

173

174

YOU'LL GET NO RESPECT FROM US IF YOU DON'T LOOK OUT FOR YOURSELF! EVEN IF YOU *ARE* RESCUING MIAKA!!

I'VE WANTED TO SAY THIS FOR SO LONG!

ANY NORMAL PERSON WOULD HAVE BEEN KILLED BY THAT LIGHTNING!

WH-WHAT'S *THAT* FOR!?

BUT...

...

YOU *KNOW* WHAT IT'S FOR! YOU NEVER SHOW AN OUNCE OF SENSE!!

...I LOST MY DAD, MY BROTHERS AND SISTERS...

...I JUST WANTED TO MAKE SURE THAT NOBODY ELSE I LOVE DIES...

...

177

Fushigi Yûgi ～7

I was given a dojinshi (fan-made comic) at a recent Fushigi Yûgi event. It was really entertaining (especially, the Nuriko story)! Thanks to Kobayashi in Chiba prefecture. A friend of mine went to the comic market (Comiket) and was totally shocked by an appearance by "Yuu Watase"! (It was someone else, apparently.) And I heard there was a dojinshi for B'z. Unlike other manga artists, I didn't launch my career with dojinshi, so I don't know that much about it (although my friends and assistants keep me informed).

But I have to say, the dojinshi shown to me are by some really impressive artists. My friends and I did put together a book of original material right around the time I was first published, but I never really got that involved in the dojinshi scene... if any of you have my book, keep in mind that it's extremely rare. But whether you're a pro or an amateur, the point is that you're drawing manga! And what matters most is that you enjoy what you're doing. It's weird that I didn't know a thing about dojinshi or yaoi comics until I was 18. What was I doing? I also want to thank the people who shared their tips for the game Streetfighter II! I was so crazy about it for a while. I wasn't playing it right.

See you all in volume 8!!

I have some extra space here to draw Chun Li in my own style. Who could this be?
AYA!! ←

I even got the cd. I can get so easily addicted.

I THINK THE THUNDERCLOUDS ARE ALSO SEIRYU WARDS!

THEY'RE BLOCKING ME FROM SENSING MIAKA'S PRESENCE!

...I DON'T KNOW WHERE TO BEGIN.

TAMAHOME, YOU'D BETTER *NOT* LOOK OVER HERE!

I'M NOT DOING ANYTHING!

ARE YOU GUYS LISTENING TO ME?

KANG-LIN!

KLOPPA
KLOPPA

WATCH OUT!!

"...KANG-LIN HAS PASSED AWAY."

"LIU-CHUAN..."

IT'S NOT TRUE!! KANG-LIN ISN'T DEAD!!

"IT'S BEST TO FORGET ABOUT HER... YOU *MUST* FORGET!"

"SHE'S *GONE!* SHE WON'T BE BACK."

WE'LL ALWAYS BE TOGETHER, KANG-LIN!!

NO! IT'S NOT *TRUE!*

YOU'LL LIVE ON, INSIDE ME.

...

AND SO YOU TURNED... HOMO?

I BECAME MY SISTER!

PLEASE! CALL ME GENDER FUL-FILLED!

I COULDN'T ACCEPT KANG-LIN'S DEATH.

I FELT THAT AS LONG AS I DRESSED LIKE A GIRL, SHE WAS STILL ALIVE...

BUT SERIOUSLY, MAYBE IT'S ABOUT TIME I...

"WE *HAVE* TO STAY ALIVE!! WE MAY LOOK BACK AT THIS AND LAUGH SOMEDAY..."

OH, THAT?

THANKS SO MUCH, NURIKO! YOU REALLY PROVED YOURSELF.

WHISPER

IT'S ALL YOUR FAULT, YOU KNOW!!

EH?

I JUST FIGURED I HAD TO LIGHT A FIRE UNDER TAMAHOME'S REAR SOMEHOW.

THAT WAY STRUCK ME FIRST...

GET DOWN EVERYONE!! WE'RE ABOUT TO BE BEACHED ON AN ISLAND!!

DADOOM

THE SHIP HAS SUFFERED A LOT OF DAMAGE. WE'LL BE HERE FOR A WHILE.

NO DA.

NOW WE'RE WASHED ASHORE ON AN ISLAND FAR FROM BEI-JIA!

A HAND?

YEAH, BUT LOOK! THE THUNDER-CLOUD'S GONE!

WHAT IS THIS PLACE!?

YAAH!!

THIS ARMOR... IT'S ONE OF *OUR* SOLDIERS! HE MUST'VE BEEN WASHED OFF THE SHIP!!

TO BE CONTINUED IN VOLUME 8: FRIEND

EDITOR'S RECOMMENDATIONS

If you enjoyed this volume of **fushigi yûgi**™ then here's some more manga you might be interested in.

Imadoki! Nowadays

In this popular Yuu Watase series, Tanpopo Yamazaki finds life at exclusive Meio Academy out of her league. The aristocratic student body snubs her, and the cute boy she noticed won't even acknowledge her existence. Still, she hopes to have some fun by starting a gardening committee, but will this help her survive in a school where superficiality reigns supreme?

Boys Over Flowers

Meet Tsukushi Makino, a poor girl at exclusive Eitoku Academy who becomes the target of the school bullies—four extremely rich and good-looking guys known as the F4. But when Tsukushi decides to bully them back, the F4 may have finally met their match!

Hot Gimmick

Sixteen-year-old Hatsumi Narita lives with her family in an apartment complex ruled over by the wealthy and much-feared Mrs. Tachibana. When the Tachibanas' domineering son, Ryoki, stumbles onto a Narita family secret, he agrees to keep it to himself—but only if Hatsumi becomes his "slave"!

The Fushigi Yûgi Guide to Sound Effects

Most of the sound effects in FUSHIGI YÛGI are the way Yuu Watase created them, in their original Japanese.

We created this glossary for a page-by-page, panel-by-panel explanation of the action and background noises. By using this guide, you may even learn some Japanese.

The glossary lists page and panel number. For example, page 1, panel 3, would be listed as 1.3.

CHAPTER FORTY-ONE:
THE MYSTERY OF "THE UNIVERSE OF THE FOUR GODS"

CHAPTER FORTY-TWO:
REMINISCENCE OF THE FUTURE

COMPLETE OUR SURVEY AND LET US KNOW WHAT YOU THINK!

☐ Please do NOT send me information about VIZ products, news and events, special offers, or other information.

☐ Please do NOT send me information from VIZ's trusted business partners.

Name: _____

Address: _____

City: _____ **State:** _____ **Zip:** _____

E-mail: _____

☐ Male ☐ Female **Date of Birth** (mm/dd/yyyy): ___ / ___ / ___ (Under 13? Parental consent required)

What race/ethnicity do you consider yourself? (please check one)

☐ Asian/Pacific Islander ☐ Black/African American ☐ Hispanic/Latino

☐ Native American/Alaskan Native ☐ White/Caucasian ☐ Other: _____

What VIZ product did you purchase? (check all that apply and indicate title purchased)

☐ DVD/VHS _____

☐ Graphic Novel _____

☐ Magazines _____

☐ Merchandise _____

Reason for purchase: (check all that apply)

☐ Special offer ☐ Favorite title ☐ Gift

☐ Recommendation ☐ Other _____

Where did you make your purchase? (please check one)

☐ Comic store ☐ Bookstore ☐ Mass/Grocery Store

☐ Newsstand ☐ Video/Video Game Store ☐ Other: _____

☐ Online (site: _____)

What other VIZ properties have you purchased/own? _____

_____

How many anime and/or manga titles have you purchased in the last year? How many were VIZ titles? (please check one from each column)

ANIME
- [ ] None
- [ ] 1-4
- [ ] 5-10
- [ ] 11+

MANGA
- [ ] None
- [ ] 1-4
- [ ] 5-10
- [ ] 11+

VIZ
- [ ] None
- [ ] 1-4
- [ ] 5-10
- [ ] 11+

I find the pricing of VIZ products to be: (please check one)

- [ ] Cheap
- [ ] Reasonable
- [ ] Expensive

What genre of manga and anime would you like to see from VIZ? (please check two)

- [ ] Adventure
- [ ] Comic Strip
- [ ] Science Fiction
- [ ] Fighting
- [ ] Horror
- [ ] Romance
- [ ] Fantasy
- [ ] Sports

What do you think of VIZ's new look?

- [ ] Love It
- [ ] It's OK
- [ ] Hate It
- [ ] Didn't Notice
- [ ] No Opinion

Which do you prefer? (please check one)

- [ ] Reading right-to-left
- [ ] Reading left-to-right

Which do you prefer? (please check one)

- [ ] Sound effects in English
- [ ] Sound effects in Japanese with English captions
- [ ] Sound effects in Japanese only with a glossary at the back

THANK YOU! Please send the completed form to:

NJW Research
42 Catharine St.
Poughkeepsie, NY 12601